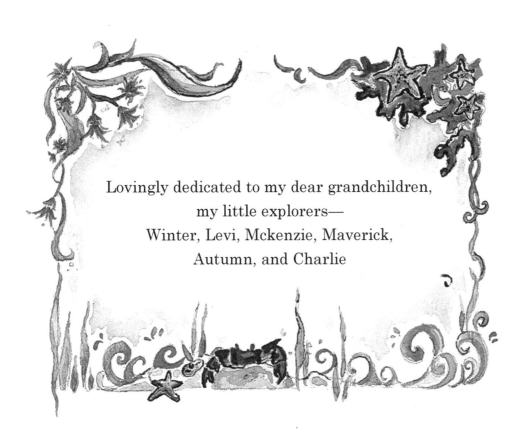

Lovingly dedicated to my dear grandchildren,
my little explorers—
Winter, Levi, Mckenzie, Maverick,
Autumn, and Charlie

Design by L.L. Kuhlmann, Two Trees Studio

Calmly gliding in the
warm tropical sea;
the silver shortfin Mako
mesmerizes me.

Metallic blue,
torpedo in shape,
an endangered species
may sport 2,000 pounds
in weight.

Filtering nostrils
with olfactory sense,
Mako detects blood
and the presence of fish.

An endothermic body
to regulate his warmth,
Mako shark is remarkably
the fastest shark on earth.

Mako leaps out of the ocean—
one, two, three—
an impressive jumper,
gaining momentum repeatedly.

Sharp nosed, streamlined,
and eyeing his prey,
Mako smiles for the biologists,
then strikes at the entrée.

Mako chomps on his mackerel;
What a great feast!
He's sure to eat it all
with 12 rows of teeth.

Sometimes it gets ugly
with the tearing of fish—
one might see fins, blood,
guts, and bits.

Why are Makos ravenous
MOST of the time?
Because of their exercise, it is
ALWAYS LUNCHTIME!

Silently, quietly
Mako goes on his way,
exploring the ocean, his home—
a splendid place to live and play.

Quick Facts about the shortfin Mako Shark

- Species: Isurus oxyrinchus
- Family: Mackerel shark
- Relatives: Longfin mako and the great white shark
- Metallic blue skin feels like sandpaper with a smooth, white underside
- Pointed snout with long gill slits
- Grows to an average length of 10 ft (3 m); females longer than males
- Razor sharp teeth—up to 12 rows—that stick out from their jaw
- Swims approximately 36 miles (60 k) for food daily
- Reproduction: Females at the age of 18 and males at 8 years; eggs develop inside the mother, with 4 to 18 pups born after 15- to 18-months
- Excellent hunters, feeding on squid, mackerel, swordfish, tuna, other sharks and birds on the surface of the ocean
- Predators: groups of dolphins, swordfish, and larger shark species
- Inhabit warm tropical offshore waters at 62.6–68°F (16–20°C); can survive in 41–51.8°F (5–11°C)
- Leaps 20–30 ft. (6–9 m) out of the water (as tall as a giraffe or far as a double-decker London bus)
- Can swim up to 60 miles per hour (97 k).
- Lives 28–35 years in the wild.

What does it mean?

- Biologists: researchers and scientists
- Detects: to discover
- Endangered: vulnerable without protective barriers
- Endothermic: to regulate body temperature and absorb heat needed for energy
- Entrée: the main course of a meal
- Filtering: a screen which material is passed through
- Impressive: to inspire and fill with excitement
- Mackerel: a sea fish
- Mesmerizes: bedazzled or spellbound
- Metallic: resembling metal with shimmering, reflective bits
- Momentum: to spark enthusiasm
- Nostrils: the inside walls of the two openings in the nose
- Olfactory sense: nerves in the nose that smell scents
- Prey: a hunted target, usually food
- Regulate: to continually bring to order
- Remarkably: to amaze and astonish
- Repeatedly: again and again; over and over
- Species: a biological class or kind
- Streamlined: sleek and taut
- Torpedo: a tube-shaped, self-propelled underwater missile
- Tropical: a climate that is warm because it's near the equator
- Underneath: below an object

References

Courtesy NOAA Fisheries, National Oceanic & Atmospheric Administration. U.S. Department of Commerce Pacific, Shortfin Mako Shark
Merriam-Webster, https://www.merriam-webster.com/dictionary. Accessed 30 Nov. 2020

CPSIA information can be obtained
at www.ICGtesting.com
Printed in the USA
BVHW021008160221
600245BV00014B/429